A Leaf for Bongani

a novelette by
CLAIRE ISHI AYETORO

equalage
PUBLISHING

www.nhnovels.com

ISBN 9781737363163 (color hbk.)

Design by Amber Henry
Cover art by Mayer Mustafa
Interior illustrations by Mayer Mustafa
Edited by Christine Taylor

www.nhnovels.com

For a vulnerable species

Swahili Words & Phrases

Mama	Mama
Bibi	Grandmother
Shangazi	Aunt
Binamu	Cousin
Mpwa	Nephew
Dada	Sister
Mpwenda	My Dear
Baba	Father
Upendo	Love
Kukimbia	Run
Binti	Daughter
Mjukuu	Grandson
Muumba	Creator
Mtoto	Baby
Wavulana	Boys
Sio mtoto wangu	Not my child
Siwezi kuvumilia hili	I cannot bear this

1

*C*ongo. The African sun, half hidden, dips in an orange-red haze. Thick, moist air pervades the atmosphere, and baobab trees sprinkle the savannah. The soft sound of hooves crunching emanates from the tall grass. A herd of Kordofan giraffe.

"Mama Bamidele?"

"Yes, my dear Bongani?"

"I'm tired."

Bamidele laughs gently at her young bull. "The sun is sinking, my dear. It will be time for rest soon. We must keep pace for now."

Their hooves are connected to long, knobby, lanky legs. Short tails flip as the giants saunter across the savannah. The majestic creatures are unmistakable beings, with their towering necks and brown patterned bodies. Bibi Barika nudges her grandson along, bending her long neck to Bongani's bottom.

"No time for complaining, dear Bongani," says Barika.

Shangazi Hadiza and Binamu Izara are close in step. Their friend Ramala and her

A Leaf for Bongani

young bull Abasi join them for the length of their journey.

"Where are we going again?" questions Bongani.

"We are headed to the land of the acacia," says Mama Bamidele.

"Where is that?"

"It is north, my dear, farther north from where we are now."

The rainy season has come to its end. It is time to move where the rains are going—soon drought will visit where they have departed. With drought, food and water will become scarce.

Hadiza sympathizes with her mpwa. "Bongani may be forbidden to complain, but I feel his pain. I'm tired too, little one."

Barika speaks with a look of sadness on her face, "I remember when we took this journey long ago. We had many more members and far less grumblers. But those days are far gone." Barika, though she looks back on old times, can wish for nothing more than to be surrounded by family and friends as she is at that moment. Times have indeed changed and are more burdensome than before. Years ago, herds had been as large as thirty or more bodies. Now, they make their trek with only seven. Nevertheless, the herd continues gracefully across the plains, making their way toward the promised land of the acacia.

Abasi grunts, "What's so special about acacia anyway? There are plenty of other plants for us to eat."

Ramala responds thoughtfully, "When you know what's best, son, you go for it."

"Words of wisdom, Ramala," says Barika. "The acacia tree offers us the best nutrition. We can be a bit picky when it comes to our diet as well."

All the ladies share a quiet giggle, knowing that Barika's words are truth.

The sun sinks further and further into the sea of sky as the herd moves along at a steady pace. Now dusk, it is time to find a place to settle for the night. They find a place amongst the baobab trees. Izara does her routine patrol. She walks in the tall grass of the surrounding area, looking for signs of lions, hyenas, and other animals that might bring them harm. No

A Leaf for Bongani

predators in sight. This is where they will sleep
tonight. The herd curls up on the spot of ground
in the high grass, and all bow their heads,
except Bongani and Abasi. They suddenly
have newfound energy and begin to romp and
play. This is acceptable so long as they stay
close.

The morning is misty. The sun has risen
higher in the sky than birds can fly. The herd
has survived the night. Now, it is time to do the
work of feeding. There are plenty of trees and
shrubs around for this activity. They aren't
acacias, but they will fill their empty bellies for
now.

"Wake up, Bongani. Time for breakfast,
dear." Barika makes the wake-up call to the
herd. If they hurry, they can catch the dew on
the leaves of the bush—extra water for their
hydration. They are good on water for now
though. They do not absolutely need to drink
but every two or three days because their
bodies are so efficient. Everyone wakes from
their slumber and stands to stretch their long,
lanky, knobby legs. The herd disperses through

the bush, but not too far apart. The little ones stay with their mothers. At most, there are two to a tree. The younger giraffe have breakfast in the lower limbs, while the older have breakfast in the higher ones.

"Mama Bamidele?" says Bongani.

"Yes, dear?"

"I like eating. It makes my belly feel full and warm."

"Food is very good for you, dear Bongani."

"Where does food come from?"

"Bongani, all good things come from Creator."

"What is Creator?"

"Creator is maker of all things. Big things and small things. Things we see, and things we cannot see."

"Where is Creator? I have never seen them."

"You see them all around you. Creator is part of us all. Because you are, I am."

Bongani thinks about this saying from Bamidele. This is a big idea.

The herd spends a considerable amount of time browsing and eating from the trees with their long, purple tongues feeling out the most tender leaves. Izara, the first to finish, finds the largest, tallest tree she can find. She stands under the tree in the shade to begin the process of ruminating, or digesting, her food. Giraffe are affectionate beings and love to ruminate together. It makes them feel close. As the others finish, one by one and two by two, they arrive at the ruminating tree.

"Bibi Barika?"

"Yes, dear Bongani?"

"Can you please tell us a story?" Bongani loves hearing stories from Barika, and Barika loves to tell them.

"Yes, dear Bongani." Barika begins her tale.

"A long, long time ago, far in the distant past, before even I was born, the earth was an empty piece of land. There was nothing here. No giraffe, no elephant, no lion. The sun would sink and rise in the sea of sky. The moon and stars would light up the night, but there was no one and nothing to enjoy it. Then, one day, a flood of stars fell from the sky onto the earth. It began to rain water on the earth for one hundred days. The sun rose and sank, rose and sank. When all of the water finally dried up, the landscape had changed. There were two of everything. Two giraffe, two elephant, two lion, two bush, and much, much more. There was grass and trees and bodies everywhere. Each being after its kind produced more of its kind until now, you see all of what there is to see."

"We came from the stars, Bibi?"

"Yes, dear Bongani. We came from the stars."

Bongani is grateful for Barika's story. It explains a lot for him. He ponders her words while he waits and ruminates.

The long walkers resume their journey. They walk a distance until they come to a large pond. They leave off their walking in favor of a drink. Their necks are so long, they cannot reach the water straight away. So, they splay their legs and bow. Now, they can get a drink.

Two pairs of eyes attached to long, bumpy, scaly snouts skim the surface of the water.

A Leaf for Bongani

"Do you see what I see, Rufaro?" one of the crocodiles says.

"I certainly do, Sizwe."

"They have two little ones with them too, Rufaro."

"I see that, Sizwe."

They wade in the water a distance away from the herd. The herd does not notice them. It has been a while since they've had a taste of water, and they drink insatiably.

"We would do well to have giraffe to eat. Their meat would last us several days." Sizwe imagines how succulent giraffe meat would be. The crocodiles slowly wade in the water, aiming to catch the giraffe by surprise. They begin to move in stealth, creeping slowly. They are sure that they will have a mighty meal of the giraffe in only a few moments.

But not on Izara's watch. Between drinks, Izara has been watching. She is always watching. She feels it her burden to keep the herd safe.

"Crocodiles approach. It is time for us to leave," Izara warns the herd. Bamidele and Ramala nudge their bulls along. They are gone

Claire Ishi Ayetoro

before the crocodiles have waded halfway to them. Good job, Izara.

And so, the giraffe continue their journey. They walk, and walk, and walk some more, enjoying each other's company all the way.

Thoughts from Bongani

This is my first journey through the Congo. It is taking forever. We walk all day long, only taking breaks to eat and drink. I can't wait until we get to the land of the acacia. Then, we will have all the food we can eat and water we can drink. I won't have to walk so much then. I can play more with Abasi. Abasi is my good friend. We were born around the same time. I'm glad he has come with us. I have someone to talk to and play with. I don't have to listen to the women talk about boring things all the time. I love Bibi's stories though. I cannot imagine a land with nothing. No bodies? No trees? No me? I wonder if I will ever go back to the stars from which I came.

11

Stars fell to the ground below
Up sprang life to rule the earth
Ancient stars that ruled the night
Took their place on earth to show
Life is an eternal flow

2

*A*nother day of roaming the savannah. The herd has already done their morning routine of browsing leafy trees and ruminating. Now, they walk.

Hadiza speaks, "We have not run into any other herds on our way. I was hoping to socialize and make some new friends."

"We have more important things to dwell on," says Izara. "We must keep vigilant to stay safe."

"What is life if you do not live it well? There is more to it than mere survival... You are always so uptight. Relax, mpwenda," says Hadiza.

"I will relax when we reach our destination," says Izara.

"Encountering other herds is a great joy. It brings back so many memories. That is how I met your and Bamidele's baba, Hadiza," says Barika as if she is hinting at something.

"It is not as if I do not want children, Mama. I have not had many opportunities to mate," says Hadiza.

The decrease in the size and frequency of giraffe herds is responsible for this.

"Your time will come," says Barika. "I would like to enjoy a full herd before I pass on."

"I do enjoy mothering," says Ramala. "It is difficult, but it is my greatest joy. To carry on life and bring a precious soul into the world. I would not have it any other way." Ramala looks at her bull Abasi. He is growing so fast.

"I don't want any calf," says Izara. "They would slow me down."

"You may as well have been born a rock," says Hadiza.

"Now, ladies, only upendo here." Barika guides the herd to peace.

"Bibi?"

"Yes, dear Bongani?"

"I'm bored, can you please, please tell us another story?"

"Yes, dear Bongani." Barika begins her tale.

"Once upon a time, way back in the old Congo, there was a lion and a young giraffe. The lion considered himself king of the savannah. His territory extended further than the eye could see. Whatever he wanted, he took for himself. Nothing was withheld from him. One day, he came upon a young bull giraffe. The young giraffe had wandered away from his herd. He was alone with the lion, and the lion was hungry. He was sure that the young giraffe would be an easy meal. The lion said to him, 'Get into my belly.' The giraffe refused. The lion was surprised. After all, he considered himself king of the savannah, and nothing was ever denied him. Again, he said to the young giraffe, 'Get into my belly.' The giraffe again refused and replied, 'You are no king, and I am not food for you.' The lion became furious with the young giraffe. The lion ran up to the giraffe and swallowed him whole. The lion was satisfied. He got what he wanted. Then, all of a sudden, he felt extreme pain. He let out a loud roar. The young giraffe used the ossicones atop his head to tear through the lion's belly. With the lion dead, the young giraffe claimed his spot as king of the savannah."

"Bibi, was he a giraffe like me?" says Bongani.

"Yes, dear Bongani, just like you," says Barika.

"Does that mean I can be a king?"

"You are a king."

At this revelation, Bongani puffs his chest. He feels proud within himself.

The herd travels until dusk. They find a lonely spot free from predators and rest for the night. Bongani and Abasi now have time to talk about boy things. They listen to the sound of crickets chirping.

"Have you ever eaten a cricket before?" says Abazi.

"Eww, that sounds gross," says Bongani.

"I have. They have a bitter taste."

"Have you ever eaten beans?"

Bamidele cannot sleep. She is curled up on the ground, but her eyes are wide open. She listens to Abasi and Bongani conversing.

"Oh yes, I love beans. They are sweet and delicious."

"Beans are a meal fit for a king like me."

"You are no king."

"Yes I am! My bibi said so."

"She was telling a story."

A Leaf for Bongani

"I am a king. I'm gonna rule the savannah someday."

"Whoever is the tallest can be king," Abasi says, knowing that he is taller than Bongani.

"No fair!"

"I'm king, I'm king," sings Abasi.

"We are not finished growing yet. I'm gonna grow big, and tall, and strong. Bigger than you. Then, we will see who is king."

Thoughts from Bamidele

The plains are dangerous. I worry about my family, about my Bongani. What will happen to us on our journey? What will we encounter? I am grateful for Izara and her watch over us. Mama is always telling these stories. They make the trip lighter, but I worry about their effect on Bongani. They are fables, but Bongani thinks they are real. I do not want him to have false hopes and expectations about how his life will be in the Congo. Just the other day, we were almost ensnared by crocodiles. What if Izara had not seen them? What would have happened to our herd? Would we have been able to escape? I must have faith that we will make it to our destination.

Weight of worry
Spirit downcast
Longing for a world that's past
Wishing for all lives to last
To the journey's end

3

*T*he herd has set out on another leg of their journey. They have been walking for days. By now, the giraffe have covered several kilometers, hundreds of them on their way to the land of the acacia. So far, they have found plenty of food to eat and water to drink along the way. Bongani has hit his stride. He has gotten into the routine of the trek. They have heard no complaints from him as of late. Ramala and Abasi are fitting in just fine. Hadiza and Izara bump heads occasionally, but they always return to upendo. Bamidele keeps careful watch over Bongani, and Barika keeps the herd sane with her wisdom and entertaining stories.

Today, it is hot, hotter than usual in such a sunny place. The sun attacks the herd, concentrating its rays on their backs. They must be sure to get enough water during these times. Bongani and Abasi do not dare run and play during the day with it being so hot. Maybe during the night when it is cooler. You would not know of the herd's suffering. They move just as steadily and gracefully as they do on any other day. They come from a line of strong, resilient ancestors who now look down on them from the heavens with great pleasure.

Barika sings a song.

"Take me to the promised land, where troubles are no more. I go with my family, the ones that I adore. All I need is food and drink and shelter from the storm. I will 'ever eat and sleep, safe from danger's thorn. Take me to the promised land, hear my song, Creator. Hide me 'midst acacia trees; they will be my savior."

The herd walks near a stretch of puddle. No pond, but it is water nonetheless. They do not know how long it will be before they have another chance to drink. They go over to the stretch of puddle, splay their legs, and get their fill of whatever they can. They are hundreds of kilometers away from where they started and, therefore, in unfamiliar territory. They are in the midst of high grass and more densely packed bush. They must keep vigilant to stay safe. Now, everyone watches as they drink.

"Quiet, Taiwo. Look, there." A small pack of hyenas, Pulang, Taiwo, and Kes are roaming the savannah. Pulang is the first to spot the giraffe.

"I have not seen giraffe in these parts for a long time," says Kes.

"It does not matter their reason for being," says Pulang. "What matters is that we eat."

"You think we can take them?" questions Taiwo.

"Certainly, we have plenty of cover. They will not see us coming before it is too late," Pulang assures Taiwo.

The hyenas begin to move through the high grass. They walk slowly, creeping, their eyes locked on the target. They are focused. Determined. They move with such ease. They live for moments like this. The thrill of the chase.

"You giraffe are gonna be sorry you came this way," says Taiwo. He lets out a quick laugh.

"Quiet, you buffoon!" whispers Pulang.

At the stretch of puddle, Izara raises her head. She scans the perimeter. She cannot see any threat, but she knows she has heard something. She looks harder. Closer. There. She spots the hyenas.

"Kukimbia!" Izara exclaims. Izara begins to run. The herd immediately leaves off drinking and runs with Izara.

"You fool, Taiwo!" says Pulang.

The chase is on. The pack of hyenas runs after the herd. The giraffe run speedily without faltering. They must run for as long as they can, for as fast as they can if they hope to escape the hyenas. The hyenas are faster than giraffe, but Izara spotted them early. The herd has a head start. The hyenas pursue the giraffe as hard as the giraffe flee.

"Mama!" shouts Bongani.

"Run, dear Bongani, keep running!" Bamidele warns.

Abasi runs close to Ramala. Though they run at great speed, they make sure each member of the herd is together. Leave no one behind.

Barika may be the oldest of the group, but she keeps up with the herd.

"Faster!" yells Izara.

A Leaf for Bongani

The hyenas gain ground, but the giraffe press even harder, pushing their bodies to the limit. Running is the giraffe's primary mode of safety in the savannah. It is their best chance to avoid trouble. Avoiding direct conflict is always the first and best choice. The giraffe manage to stay ahead of the hyenas. Soon, the hyenas slow to a trot. Then, they stop. They will conserve their energy for another chase. The herd escapes yet another threat, thanks to Izara and their will to survive.

After the chase, the giraffe must rest before they continue on. They find a spot in the bush to collect themselves for a time.

"Mama, are they gone now?" Bongani is still fearful. This has been his first encounter with hyenas.

"Yes, dear Bongani. We are safe now," assures Bamidele.

Barika begins to sing again.

"Take me to the promised land, where troubles are no more. I go with my family, the ones that I adore. All I need is food and drink and shelter from the storm. I will 'ever eat and sleep, safe from danger's thorn. Take me to the promised land, hear my song, Creator. Hide me 'midst acacia trees; they will be my savior."

Thoughts from Barika

I am old. I have lived through three generations. I am tired, but I now live for my family. I tell stories to keep our traditions alive. They may not understand why I am always telling, but it is important. To keep alive what our ancestors gave us. To teach us how to think, how to survive, how to stay together. Our stories are what have kept me strong. I think of how life will be for them when I am passed. I hope they will remember. I hope they will stay together.

The old ones tell the story
The young ones live the glory
In time they all pass on
And leave the earth in mourning

4

"Bongani?" says Bamidele.

"Yes, Mama?"

"How are you feeling today?"

Bongani is silent. He doesn't know how he is feeling. He feels something though. Something different that he has not felt before.

"Are you happy?" says Bamidele.

"No."

"Are you sad?"

"Not that."

"Are you angry?"

"No."

"Are you scared?"

"Mmm… Maybe?"

"Tell me what is on your mind, dear."

"Well, I wonder what will happen when we are on our way. What if we come across hyenas again? What if we come across something else that wants to hurt us?"

"Ahh," says Barika. "Bongani is worried."

"Worried?" questions Bongani.

"Yes, dear Bongani. I think you are worried. That is when you think about things that have not happened and scare yourself," Barika explains.

"I am worried," says Bongani.

"Bongani, do not worry," says Bamidele. "You are protected."

Bamidele knows that she should not have made that promise. She understands the unpredictable nature of life in the Congo. There is no guarantee that Bongani will be spared on their journey. There is only the best she can do. But at this time, she sees no other way to calm Bongani's heart. So, she lies to him.

"We will protect you, Bongani, do not worry," chimes Izara.

"Is the rock melting?" jokes Hadiza.

"Hush, Hadiza," says Izara.

Hadiza and Izara smile to one another. Upendo.

Barika begins another tale.

"A pack of hyena roam in the bush. They see a herd of antelope. One hyena says to another, 'You see the antelope? They are ours. We will kill and eat them.' The hyenas are cocky. They begin to laugh. They laugh and laugh and laugh some more. They laugh so hard that they are even rolling on the ground collecting dust on their fur. When they finish laughing, one hyena says to another, 'Now, let us kill and eat.' But, when they look, there are no more antelope. They had laughed so hard and so long and so loud that the antelope heard them and ran away."

Bongani and Abasi laugh at her tale.

"In order to be protected, we must listen to what is going on around us. If we listen, we get clues that will let us know when danger is near. Then, we run like the antelope."

In all of their walking and talking, the herd has come to a large field that blocks their path. In the field, they see creatures—humans. They are beating the ground with instruments. There are not too many humans, but the giraffe are still wary.

"Humans…" says Barika. She has encountered few humans in her life, but the few times she did encounter them, they had not been good experiences.

"What should we do?" questions Ramala. Abasi steps closer to his mother. So does Bongani.

"I say we wait," offers Izara. "We wait for a while, see how they react to us."

And so, the giraffe stand. And wait. And watch.

The humans leave off working the land to look at the giraffe. They point and utter strange noises. They do not run. They do not attack. Instead, they pick up their sticks and begin to work the land again.

"Hmm... They do not pursue us," says Barika.

"Maybe it is safe to cross," says Izara.

The giraffe wait a few moments more, until Barika announces, "We will cross."

Still suspicious, the giraffe begin to cross the large field. As they walk, Bongani sniffs the air.

"Beans... sweet beans!" exclaims Bongani. A treat fit for a king. "Can we eat the beans?"

Beans would be a nice snack. The herd deserves a treat. Izara splays her legs and bows to the ground to taste the beans. The rest of the herd does the same. The giraffe graze the field and eat the beans to their fill. Before they know it, they have come to the opposite edge of the field. They have cleared their obstacle and filled their bellies all at once. Not bad.

Thoughts from Bongani

I am learning. There is much to know about life. There is danger all around. If we stick together, we can be safe. If we listen, we can know of danger. I miss the safety of the other land. I miss playing all day with Abasi. Things will get better though. I know they will. Once we reach the land of the acacia, we will not have to worry anymore.

Wishing I could laugh and play
All until day fades away
As I grow, I understand
Threat and danger fill the land
Instead, I must take a stand
My freedom to live at stake

5

*T*he heat wave persists. The herd again walks for many kilometers in the heat of the day. The journey is long, but they will know when they have reached half-way by the large pond surrounded by other herds of animals. By the looks of it, they are nearly to their checkpoint.

Looking in the distance, Izara is the first to spot the congregation. "I see a multitude of bodies," says Izara.

They are at a large pond in the middle of the savannah. But the herd still has many kilometers to go to reach the checkpoint.

"Oh, wonderful," says Barika. She is excited.

"Finally," says Hadiza. She is excited as well. Her wish has come true—they will be able to meet new friends.

"Do we have time for a story, Bibi?" asks Bongani.

"We certainly do, dear Bongani," says Barika. She begins her tale.

A Leaf for Bongani

"There once was a young giraffe named Abena. She was a curious one and wandered away from her herd. Before she knew it, she was lost in the savannah. She began to search for her family but was afraid to call out to them for fear that a lion or hyena would answer. So, she went behind every tree in sight. She looked and looked but saw no one. Abena became sad and cried to herself. She did not believe she would ever see her family again. She cried softly all day and into the night when the moon saw her crying. The moon said to the sun, 'A daughter of the stars cries from day to night. What shall we do to help her heart?' The sun replied, 'She has lost her way, so we must lead her back home. I will send help in the morning.' When morning came, the sun sent a bird. The bird flew over the sky and saw Abena's herd. They were worried for Abena. The bird flew to Abena with good news. 'Abena,' said the bird. 'I know where your family has gone. They look for you. If you follow me, I will lead you to them.' Abena stopped her crying and followed the bird. The bird flew, and Abena ran. Through the bush they went, Abena hopeful that the bird would lead her to the right place. Soon, she was reunited with her family and was filled with joy and happiness. She loved her family and vowed never to stray away again. There is no upendo like family upendo. Because you are, I am."

"We are almost there," says Hadiza.

"Can we run ahead?" asks Abasi. He is eager to get to the pond and see new faces.

"We must stay together," says Ramala.

The giraffe continue on, and after some distance, they reach the pond. Checkpoint.

There are so many herds. They have come from many different places on their journey to better lands. There are antelope, wildebeest, rhinoceros, boar, and elephants. There are even birds and other giraffe. Best of all, there are a few acacia in sight.

"First, we will eat, then we will drink," says Barika.

The herd goes to browse the acacia trees. It has been several hundred kilometers since they have had a bite to eat at one of them. You would think they are not worth the trouble.

A Leaf for Bongani

Acacia trees are tall, so not many other animals can reach their luscious leaves, but they also contain many thorns. The giraffe's tough, purple tongue keeps it from getting pricked too frequently. They find the hassle worth it.

While Bongani is eating the leaves from the tree, he notices a bird. An oxpecker.

"Hi," says Bongani.

"Hello," says the bird. "My name is Zola. What is yours?"

"I am Bongani. Where did you come from?"

"Well, I am a bird. And birds live in trees."

"I knew that."

Zola and Bongani laugh.

"Where did you come from?" says Zola.

"I came from the south. We are on our way to the land of the acacia."

"Oh, I've heard of that place, but I have never been there before."

"I haven't either, but I cannot wait to get there."

"What is it said to be like?"

Claire Ishi Ayetoro

"There are all the acacia trees you can imagine, and there is all the water you can drink. It is a paradise."

"Oh? That sounds nice. I would like to go there. Can I go with you?"

"We do not fly, we walk."

"I know that. I can ride on your back. In exchange, I will eat the bugs from your hide."

This sounds tempting to Bongani, and it will be nice to have another friend.

"Let me ask my mama."

Bongani runs to find Bamidele. Once he finds her, he asks with slight trepidation. "Mama?" says Bongani. "I met a new friend, Zola. Can she go to the land of the acacia with us?"

Bamidele thinks. She thinks some more. She looks at Bongani and gives her answer.

"Yes, Bongani. She can go with us."

"Thank you, Mama!"

Bongani dashes back to his tree.

"Mama says yes!"

"Yay!" shouts Zola.

A Leaf for Bongani

Zola hops from the tree onto Bongani's back. The herd has gained a new member and a new friend.

The herd finishes their meal. It is satisfying to have a taste of acacia again. This will last them until they reach the new land even if they do not see another on their way, but chances are they will; if they do, they will stop and eat of it again. Now, it is time to drink. The herd casually saunters to the large pond. There is much chatter around the pond. Families and friends speak with one another. The herd arrives next to a group of elephants. They begin to drink.

"Barika… Barika, is that you?" one of the elephants speaks out.

Barika looks up from her drinking.

"Asha… Asha!" exclaims Barika.

"Oh, dada, it is so good to see you again!" Asha raises her trunk to Barika's neck in greeting.

"It has been so long, dada. Meet my grandson." Barika gestures toward Bongani. Bongani is shy. He stands close to Bibi.

"Oh, what a strapping young bull he is. You must meet my granddaughter." Asha signals to her grandchild. "This is Nia."

"How lovely, Asha."

"Can we play?" asks Bongani.

"If it is okay with Nia," says Barika.

"It is okay," says Nia.

With Zola on Bongani's back, Nia, Bongani, and Abasi run off to play in sight of the herds. Asha and Barika catch up and talk about what has transpired since they last saw each other.

On another side of the pond, a herd of bull giraffe gather. They look across and see Bongani's herd. A member of the bull herd, Dalmar, addresses his friend.

"Juma, do you see what I see?"

"I do indeed. Lady giraffe."

"I see one who is of interest to me." Dalmar is a very tall giraffe. He is the tallest of his herd and is big and strong.

"I see one too," says Juma who is big and strong as well.

"We cannot both go. You know that Juma."

"Shall we have a contest?"

A Leaf for Bongani

The two bulls get ready to decide who will approach the lady herd. To do this, they will engage in a traditional brawl called necking, trading blows with their necks until one of them surrenders.

Juma and Dalmar walk away from the pond, closer to the view of the ladies. They want to get their attention. Dalmar takes the first shot. He swings his long, lanky neck across and whips Juma. His ossicones jab Juma in the neck. Next, Juma swings his long, gangly neck. Dalmar takes a blow. They continue in this fashion, swinging and colliding their necks and ossicones.

Hadiza takes notice.

"Look at those bulls, fighting. You think they are fighting over a chance to talk to us?" says Hadiza.

"I do not know, and I do not care," says Izara.

"You are no fun, binamu."

Hadiza continues to watch the bulls. She hopes that they will come over. Hadiza is not the only one who notices. Bongani and Abasi are intrigued as well. They pause their play to watch the performance.

"Whoa, Bongani! Look at those bulls!" says Abasi, amazed.

"I see them Abasi! Are they fighting?" says Bongani.

"They do this all the time. They are challenging one another for a chance to approach a female of your herd," says Nia.

"Eww, gross!" says Bongani.

Abasi agrees. But, it does look fun.

"I think it is romantic," says Zola.

"More gross!" says Bongani. They all laugh together.

The bulls are near the end of their brawl. They are winded and quite sore. Dalmar takes one last swing at Juma.

"Okay, okay Dalmar! You win," Juma concedes.

Dalmar has won, but there is no upendo lost between them. Dalmar puffs his chest. He is proud. He has earned his opportunity to talk to the female herd, and he knows just the one he wants to approach. He walks.

A Leaf for Bongani

"Izara, Izara, one of the bulls is coming over!" exclaims Hadiza.

"Eh…" responds Izara. She then walks away from the herd to the other side of the pond.

Dalmar approaches. He has his eyes set on…Hadiza.

"Hello, my name is Dalmar. May I ask your name?"

"I am Hadiza." She bats her long eyelashes.

"You are beautiful, Hadiza. Would you like to take a walk with me?"

"I would love to…"

Hadiza and Dalmar take their leave from the pond and escape into the bush.

"That was amazing!" says Abasi. "I am big bull, Abasi. I challenge you, Bongani."

"I accept your challenge!" says Bongani.

Abasi swings his neck at Bongani. Bongani swings his neck at Abasi. This does not last long though. Ramala notices the two.

"Wavulana! Boys! Stop that! You could hurt yourselves," says Ramala.

"Yes, Mama," says Abasi.

Claire Ishi Ayetoro

"Yes, Ramala," says Bongani. Bongani and Abasi look at one another and smile.

The herd spends the day having a wonderful time meeting and speaking with old and new friends. Barika and Asha renew an old bond that has stood the test of time. Bongani and Abasi make new friends with Zola and Nia. Bamidele and Ramala get a small break from watching over their bulls. Dalmar and Hadiza walk and dance together, creating a child within Hadiza's belly. And Izara... Izara enjoys a break from her constant watch over the herd. Now, the day is coming to an end. The herd decides to spend the night near the large pond before setting out in the morning.

Thoughts from Bongani

I had the best time today. I have never seen so many bodies before in one place. I made new friends in Nia and Zola. I am glad that Zola will get to travel with us to the new land. I am glad I met Nia. I will miss her, but maybe we will be reunited again like Bibi and Lady Asha. Onward to the land of the acacia!

A Leaf for Bongani

Thoughts from Bamidele

Today was wonderful. Everyone had so much fun. And I got a much needed break. To see Bongani have this experience gives me hope for what his life can be. The Congo is a dangerous place, but there are joys to be had as well. Now, Bongani sees this.

Thoughts from Barika

These are the times I live for. Seeing Asha again did so much to lift my heart and spirit. Being with her brought back so many memories of the old days. It made me feel young again.

You never know what life will bring
At times it gives you special things
Enjoy these moments when they come
Cherish them your whole life long

6

*P*it. *Pat… Pit. Pat.* The herd stirs. *Pit. Pat.* A drop of water falls squarely between Bongani's eyes. He sniffs the air, and the scent is refreshing. The gentle rumble of thunder echoes through the atmosphere. The clouds break to let out their store of water, slowly at first, then without hesitation.

"Rain!" exclaims Bongani.

It is morning, and the herd awakens to a welcome rain shower. The heat wave and surging temperatures that seized the land for days has now broken. The trio, Bongani, Abasi, and Zola on Bongani's back, rise to gallop in the falling rain.

"Bless you, Creator," says Barika. She does not know how much more of the heat she can take. The rain is a welcome change, and the herd will use it as their cover for the first leg of their journey beyond the pond. They each say their last goodbyes to Asha and Nia and begin again on their trek to the land of the acacia.

"Welcome to the herd, Zola," says Barika.

A Leaf for Bongani

"Thank you, Bibi," says Zola. "I have heard many good things about where we are going. I wonder what can be out there for me."

"And you, Hadiza," says Barika. "I saw you walking into the bush with that bull."

Hadiza blushes.

"I suspect I will have another mjukuu on the way." Barika looks in Hadiza's direction and smiles.

Hadiza is silent, embarrassed by her mother's forwardness.

The herd journeys for kilometers, for days, eating and drinking what they can find along the way, and listening to the grand and wise tales from Bibi Barika's store. Then, they see a sign that they have crossed over the threshold into a new and more dangerous place. There is a foul smell that permeates the air, and the dreadful sight confirms their notion.

"Bongani, Abasi, look away," says Barika.

The sight is too much for anyone, let alone the young. There is an elephant. He does not move. His leg is caught in a metal trap, and he is missing his long, beautiful, white tusks.

Claire Ishi Ayetoro

"This is the work of humans," says Barika. The humans she is referring to are known as poachers. They set traps for animals and ambush them for their meat and hides. For elephants, they remove their tusks. For giraffe, they remove their tails. When Barika was younger, giraffe were not a target for poachers. But now, giraffe are high on the poachers' list as a hot commodity. Now, the herd not only needs to look out for animal predators, but human predators too. The herd walks in silence, the air of whimsy they enjoyed replaced with the pain of worry.

Thoughts from Barika

I have seen this before. The senseless waste of bodies, taken away from their friends and families. This is why we are wary of humans. Humans take, and take, and take from us. From our land. From our life. What have we done to deserve this? We do not harm them in any way. That is not the way of our hearts. If this does not stop, there will be nothing left of us.

Who will fight for us
Who will make us free
Who will be our friend
And save our family

7

*T*he herd has been on edge since they saw the poor elephant who lost his life. To make matters worse, they have had to walk through areas more densely packed with grass and trees. This has lowered their ability to see danger approaching. They only stop when absolutely necessary, even skipping meals and water from time to time. They do their best to stay vigilant in this strange and ominous land.

"Mama?" says Bongani. "I am very hungry."

"I am hungry too, mpwa," says Hadiza.

Now, they must stop to eat something— they are famished.

"We will stop to eat. Everyone, be watchful," says Barika.

The herd, scanning the area as best they can, goes into bushes nearby to eat of their leaves. Bongani takes a bite of the leaves. Immediately, saliva gushes into his mouth. His body has been longing for a bite of food. He eats until the empty feeling in his belly goes away.

Hadiza, having eaten a good number of leaves, speaks out in relief, "Oh, I can go on now!" She along with the rest of the herd have had their fill. They have successfully refueled and are happy to continue on their way. They finish their eating, exit the bush, and stand together. There is a stillness to the atmosphere. Too still, yet an outside presence is felt among them. They are not prepared for what awaits.

The herd has not heard them coming. They have not seen them. How can they have missed them?

Two lions stand in their midst. If they had seen them coming, noticed them before, they would have had the opportunity to run. But the lions are too close now. Running is a sure way to lose a member of the herd. Now, they must stand. And fight.

"Leave us," says Barika. She stands bold within the herd. No one moves a muscle.

"That won't be possible," says Sura, the leading lioness.

A Leaf for Bongani

"You will not leave here without wounds," says Bamidele.

"We will take our chances," says Ime, second in command.

There is a standoff between the giraffe and the lions, each waiting for the other to make the first move. Bongani is stunned. Abasi is nervous.

"Everyone, stay still," says Barika. But, Abasi cannot control himself. He takes off into a gallop.

"Abasi, no!" shouts Ramala.

Ime takes off after Abasi. Ramala takes off after Ime. Abasi runs as fast as he can, but he is not fast enough. Ime overtakes him. Ramala catches up, but it is too late.

Sura stalks Barika and her family. Bongani is terrified. He is the smallest of the group, making him the target. Sura makes a break for Bongani. She snatches at his legs, but Bamidele immediately intervenes. She begins to kick at Sura with her long legs. Sura backs away, but Bamidele pursues her. Bamidele begins to trample Sura under her hooves. Sura roars as Bamidele's strong legs crush her; then,

Claire Ishi Ayetoro

Sura lies motionless on the ground. There is no more roaring from Sura.

Soon after, Ramala returns to the herd. Alone.

***

The herd walks. They are downcast. Ramala is in sorrow and weeps.

"Where is Abasi?" asks Bongani.

No one speaks.

"Where is Abasi!" Bongani demands.

"Abasi is no more," says Barika.

"You do not know that, Bibi!" shouts Bongani. He begins to cry. "We did not even look for him!" shouts Bongani amidst bitter tears.

Bongani knows in his heart what he does not want to believe. He will not see Abasi anymore.

The herd walks until nightfall. There are no stories from Bibi. No talking from anyone. Izara is disappointed in herself. She had not spotted the danger. She had not protected the herd. That night, instead of sleeping, there is mourning.

A Leaf for Bongani

"Hummmm…..Hummmm….hummm," Barika hums softly to mourn Abasi. "Hummmm……" She continues her humming for the better part of the night. The herd is comforted.

Thoughts from Bongani

I miss Abasi. I miss my homeland. I wish we never set out on this journey. I no longer wish for the land of the acacia with no Abasi. I wish he could break out of the lion's belly just like in Bibi's story. Then, he could be here with me. I am scared, and I am worried. Will we even make it there with who we have left? Will there be Mama and Bibi anymore?

What is it worth
To journey to a land
If there is no family
If there is no friend
We should be together
That's how it should be
Standing in our circle
Around acacia trees

8

"Wandering, in savannah land. Sun on my head, no cloud in the sky. Drink at the pond and drink it dry. Step my hooves from sun up to night. Oh, savannah land. Terrible foe and wonderful friend. Terrible start with a wonderful end. We won't stop, we flow with the wind." Barika sings alone, but Bamidele, Hadiza, and Izara soon join her.

"Wandering, in savannah land. Sun on my head, no cloud in the sky. Drink at the pond and drink it dry. Step my hooves from sun up to night. Oh, savannah land. Terrible foe and wonderful friend. Terrible start with a wonderful end. We won't stop, we flow with the wind."

"Give me life and give me peace. Let the pain and struggle cease. I will fight and I will stand, while I wander savannah land. Wandering, in savannah land. Kicking up the dust and sand. Eat the bush and flee the man, in savannah land."

A Leaf for Bongani

The herd travels further into the savannah, but they do not walk with as much strength as they had before. The wind blows across the landscape, folding the tall grass under its force. The sun shines down relentlessly, but the wind softens its landing.

"When will we get there?" asks Bongani.

"The way is not much longer, dear Bongani," says Bamidele.

The herd is weary. The burden of worry weighs heavily on them, and the loss of Abasi withers their spirits. They continue to press on in spite of it all.

"I wonder if we should have ever started this journey," says Ramala. She is bitter. She has felt the loss of her son greater than them all.

"Would you have us turn back now?" says Izara.

"My family is gone. This is your journey now. Mine has ended." Ramala speaks in her sorrow—she does not reason well.

"I will not hear of this," says Barika. "We must continue. Together. Ramala, you will stay with us. We are your family now. You are grafted into our tree."

"Mama is right," says Hadiza. "We cannot turn around now. What do we have to go back to?"

There is no way to tell if it will be more dangerous to turn around or to keep going, but there will be nothing for them in their home land once the dry season sets in. They have to gamble on making it to their destination.

"Dear Bongani," says Barika. "Would you like to hear a story?"

"Yes, Bibi. I need a story," says Bongani.

Barika begins her tale.

"At one time, there was a herd of giraffe. They had bulls and cows tall and short. They came to a tall, tall acacia tree. The tree was so tall that even the tallest bull in the herd could not reach it. They did not know how they would get to the leaves at the top. Then, the youngest bull had an idea. 'If we work together, we can reach the leaves,' he said. The tallest bull replied, 'I am the tallest bull, and even I cannot reach the top. How do you propose we do this?' The young bull said, 'If we climb one on top of the other, we can reach the top.' The herd came together in a line. They began to climb one on top of the other, standing on each other's back. The last to climb was the young bull. When he made it to the top, he was able to reach the leaves. He took a leaf from the tree and passed it down to the one below him. The one below him passed the leaf down to the next in line and so on. The young bull picked and passed leaves until everyone in the herd had their fill, including him."

"I could use an acacia leaf right now," says Bongani.

"There is a leaf for Bongani," says Barika. "But, we must keep going. If we stick together and work together, there is nothing we cannot achieve."

Barika begins to sing, and everyone joins together.

"Wandering, in savannah land. Sun on my head, no cloud in the sky. Drink at the pond and drink it dry. Step my hooves from sun up to night. Oh, savannah land. Terrible foe and wonderful friend. Terrible start with a wonderful end. We won't stop, we flow with the wind… Give me life and give me peace. Let the pain and struggle cease. I will fight, and I will stand, while I wander savannah land. Wandering, in savannah land. Kicking up the dust and sand. Eat the bush and flee the man, in savannah land."

The herd walks on with new courage. They are refreshed, but there is still present danger. They keep a watchful eye and hopeful hearts as they journey through the savannah. Whatever they face, they will be okay as long as they stand together. The herd walks 'til nightfall. They find a spot to sleep and drift away.

***

"Abasi? Abasi, is that you?"

"Hello, my friend Bongani."

"Abasi, I thought I would never see you again!"

"I know, that stinking lion got me, but I am okay now. I am in the land of my ancestors. I do not hurt here. I am safe."

"Abasi, I miss you."

"I miss you too, Bongani."

"Will we ever play again?"

A Leaf for Bongani

"We will play again one day, but not soon; you must live your life. Then, we will be together again."

"Bongani… Bongani," says Bamidele. She dips her head and nudges Bongani. He has been sleeping. Now he is awake. It is morning. Time to get moving.

Thoughts from Bamidele

We have suffered great loss. Bongani has lost a great friend. At first, I did not agree with Mama's stories, but now, I see their worth. She has soothed the hearts of us all and has helped us to gain courage in a time of great need. We still have some ways to go. There is still trouble lurking in the savannah. I do not know what will happen, but I am at peace.

In the struggle, I find peace
Though the struggle does not cease
It's a calm within a storm
Shelter where I'm safe and warm
Still, I watch for danger's thorn

9

"*H*adiza, how are you holding up?" asks Bamidele.

"Oh, I am managing just fine. The baby in my belly is not big enough yet," says Hadiza.

"I wonder if it will be a bull or cow."

"I am hoping for a binti."

"A binti would be special," says Zola.

"Your belly will grow for five seasons. Then, you will have a precious child," says Barika. "I will love my new mjukuu, just like I love my dear Bongani." Barika looks at Bongani with soft eyes. Her pride and joy.

"I will be a binamu!" says Bongani.

"Yes, you will be a cousin," says Hadiza with a smile.

They walk along with a sense of cheer that they have not had for a while. But the land is still dangerous and tricky, so they better watch their steps. They have witnessed what happens to the elephant when they cross the threshold, and they are not immune to that fate. And so, they continue on.

A Leaf for Bongani

"Ouch!" exclaims Hadiza. She lets out a dreadful moan.

"Oof!" exclaims Ramala.

Two loud snapping sounds emanate from the grass. The herd pauses.

"What is the matter?" asks Barika, with much concern.

"My hoof. It is stuck. I cannot move, and it hurts badly," says Hadiza.

"Mine is the same," says Ramala. "I cannot move."

Barika lowers her head to inspect the ground. Her heart drops at what she finds.

"Oh, Muumba!" exclaims Barika. "Sio mtoto wangu! Not my child!"

Barika finds that Hadiza and Ramala have walked into metal traps. Into snares set by… poachers.

"What can we do? Ouch!" says Ramala as she tries to move her leg. The metal snare is made of barbed wire. When she moves her leg, the wire digs into her skin. Barika moves around in a nervous shuffle. She tries to bite at the snare, but the barbed wire hurts her mouth.

"Muumba!" shouts Barika. "Siwezi kuvumilia hili! I cannot bear this!"

Barika tries, but there is nothing she can do. There is nothing any of them can do. The snare cannot be undone.

The herd stands and weeps.

Barika knows what will happen to Hadiza and Ramala. Soon, humans will come to them. They will not be spared.

Barika begins to sing through her tears.

"Oh, Creator, hear my heart. Bless the children of the stars. Let them see the promised land. Help them see it where they stand. We will meet again someday. But here, now, we cannot stay. Bless the children of the stars, oh, Muumba."

The herd continues to weep. They know that now, they must part ways. If the rest of them stay, none of them will be spared. They do not have much time, but they try to comfort Hadiza and Ramala.

"My sister," says Bamidele. "Because you are, I am. Because I am, you are. We will see one another on the other side." Bamidele rubs

A Leaf for Bongani

her long neck against Hadiza's. She stands close to her sister.

"Ramala, my daughter," says Barika. "You have been grafted into our family tree. Because you are, I am, and because I am, you are. You will see the promised land." Barika rubs her long neck against Ramala's.

"I see humans," says Izara. She sees them coming up in trucks, driving in the grass. An ambush.

"Barika, Bamidele, Bongani, you must go now. I will stay and try to fight them off."

Loud gunfire is heard, and the humans yell a war cry.

Bamidele, Barika, and Bongani gallop away.

***

They are now well out of sight of the poachers and of the three they left behind. They are tired from all their running. They stop to catch their breath.

"Ouch!" shouts Bongani.

"Bongani! What happened?" urges Bamidele.

Bongani begins to run around, bucking his legs. Something has stung him.

"I do not know, Mama!" he shouts.

Bongani begins to feel woozy, sleepy. He tries to fight the feeling, but soon, he drops to the ground, unconscious.

"Bongani!" shouts Zola. She does not know what is happening. She flies off Bongani into a tree.

"Ouch!" shouts Bamidele.

"Oof!" shouts Barika.

Soon after, Bongani is on the ground, surrounded by humans. There is a blanket covering his eyes, but he knows it is them. He hears the strange sounds coming from them. The humans are looping ropes around his body. His heart beats at a wild pace. They pour cool water onto him and rub his head. When they are done, they help Bongani to his feet. Bongani tries to flee, but the ropes keep him from doing so. The humans guide him into a box on the back of a truck. His eyes are still covered. The truck cranks with Bongani on it and drives off to an unknown place.

Thoughts from Bongani

Help me! Someone help me... Muumba, I need you now! I am scared. I do not know what is happening. I am in the hands of humans. Bibi says that is never a good thing. What will happen to me now? Mama is not here to protect me... I must be strong. I must believe. That is what Bibi would tell me. That is what a king would do.

I look to wisdom from the past
Through words spoken, deep and vast
Help me to believe the truth
Though I falter, in my youth

10

*A*fter a long while, the truck stops, and the engine is cut. A human removes the mask from Bongani's face. *Where am I?* They lead him into a wooden enclosure, a boma, in an area shaded with trees. The space is large, and he has room to move around. *Where is Mama? Where is Bibi?* Bongani is alone in the boma, but not for long.

"Bongani!" Zola arrives.

"Zola!" shouts Bongani. "I am so happy to see you!"

"I am happy to see you too!"

"How did you get here?"

"I flew! I followed the humans overhead. I had to know where you were going."

"Thank you for finding me, Zola."
Zola flies into one of the trees inside the boma.

"Have you seen Mama and Bibi?" asks Bongani.

"I have not seen them…" replies Zola.

Bongani looks downcast. He now worries.

A human walks over to the boma. He sets out something. Bongani walks over to it. He

A Leaf for Bongani

sniffs. There is water, and there are beans, sweet beans. Bongani is hungry, and he is tired. He knows that he is to be wary of humans, but his belly cannot resist. Bongani eats the beans. It makes his belly happy, although his head is not. Bongani spends the night alone, no Mama, no Bibi. Zola is his only company, but he appreciates her presence. He has never been this alone in his entire life. He has always been with someone. Now, there is no one. Bongani wishes for a story from Bibi or comfort from his mama. The night is quiet and still. He only hears the sound of crickets chirping. He lies on the ground and waits for what comes next. He is glad to be safe from predators, at least, with plenty of food to eat and water to drink inside the boma.

Bongani begins to sing a song that his bibi sang to him.

"Take me to the promised land, where troubles are no more. I go with my family, the ones that I adore. All I need is food and drink and shelter from the storm. I will 'ever eat and sleep, safe from danger's thorn. Take me to the promised land, hear my song, Creator. Hide me 'midst acacia trees; they will be my savior."

***

There is a commotion. Bongani becomes alert. The door to the boma opens.

"Mama!" shouts Bongani. Bongani runs up to his mother.

"Bongani, my mtoto! My baby!" shouts Bamidele.

"Mama, I missed you!"

"I missed you too, Bongani. Are you okay?" Bamidele inspects every inch of Bongani's body.

"I am okay!" says Bongani.

"Oh, Bongani!" Barika is also present.

"Bibi!" shouts Bongani.

Bongani runs to his bibi. They embrace their necks. The family has been reunited in the boma. They are together again.

"Come, eat and drink! There is plenty!" Bongani leads Barika and Bamidele to the beans and water that have been set out.

"Thank you, dear Bongani," says Barika. "We are very hungry."

A Leaf for Bongani

Barika and Bamidele eat of the beans and drink of the water.

"Where are we?" asks Bongani.

"We do not know, Bongani," says Bamidele. "We do not know."

No one knows where they are, but they are glad to be together again. They are also glad to have food and protection. They do not know what is to come, but they are safe, for now.

Thoughts from Bongani

I am caught in a whirlwind. I do not know what is happening. We have lost half our herd. Half lost to humans and the other half gained by humans. What do they want with us? Why do they keep us trapped? I am happy for beans and water. Abasi would have loved to have all the beans he could eat. I wonder if we will ever make it to the land of the acacia now.

Thoughts from Barika

I am torn. I have lost pieces of my heart. My Hadiza, my Izara, and my Ramala. We started the journey with seven. Now, we are only three. Worse, we are in the hands of humans. This is never good. We cannot run. We cannot fight. We are at their mercy. May Creator have mercy on us.

Thoughts from Bamidele

I am with my Bongani, my baby. I thought we were parted forever, but I see him now. He is safe and unharmed. Creator is with us.

We look to hope
It's all we have
To reach our journey's end
We hope that hope will see us through
Our freedom we will win

11

*I*n the morning, the humans come. They lead the herd out of the boma and into a large truck. Zola flies onto Bongani's back. The truck starts and begins to move.

"Where are we going?" asks Bongani.

"Only Muumba knows," says Barika.

The truck drives for many hours. The herd rides through the Congo, then out of the Congo. The truck is loaded onto a barge, and they cross a long, wide river. The herd looks out at the sight in wonder. So far, they have only seen much of the same: trees, trucks, and humans. More humans than they have wanted to see. But they have never before floated on water.

"Wow, I have never seen so much water," says Bongani.

"Neither have I," says Bamidele.

After crossing the river, they travel dirt roads and enter a new bush. The truck comes to a stop, and the engine cuts. The back of the truck is opened. The herd stands still. No humans come to them. No humans try to bind them with ropes or lead them anywhere.

"What do we do?" asks Bongani.

"We run," says Barika.

The herd runs out of the truck. No one chases after them, but they run until they feel no presence of the humans anymore.

They explore their surroundings. They are in a strange, new land. They walk through the bush to understand where they are. They wander for a while, coming to the edge of the bush. When they exit the bush, they are amazed at what they see. They have come to a land where there are acacia trees as far as their eyes can see. Many herds surround a pond with plenty of water to drink. There are elephants, hippos, buffalo, rhinos, zebras, and even giraffe. This is better than the land they had sought. Much more than they could have dreamed of. There is more than one leaf for Bongani. There are many, many leaves for Bongani.

"Bibi, we made it!" says Bongani.

"We are here!" sings Zola.

A Leaf for Bongani

"Creator has heard and seen us," says Barika.

Bongani takes off in a gallop. He runs through the new savannah. His new home. Together, with his family.

Take me to the promised land, where troubles are no more. I go with my family, the ones that I adore. All I need is food and drink and shelter from the storm. I will 'ever eat and sleep, safe from danger's thorn. Take me to the promised land, hear my song, Creator. Hide me 'midst acacia trees; they will be my savior.

The End

Afterword

I hope you have enjoyed your reading of *A Leaf for Bongani*. This book was written to highlight the plight of giraffes in the wild. It is estimated that only roughly 90,000 giraffes populate the world today, due to habitat loss, predation, and poaching. Only we can stop their "silent extinction."

Because you are, I am. This is an idea straight from Ubuntu, a southern African philosophy of togetherness. It means that our only way to live freely is to work together in community. We are each a reflection of one another, and therefore, we must treat each other with respect and dignity.

Acha uende kwa upendo. May you go forth in love.

Also by
Claire Ishi Ayetoro

I Hear the Black Raven: A Petite Memoir

CPSIA information can be obtained
at www.ICGtesting.com
Printed in the USA
LVHW070335090222
710633LV00006B/72

.